An independent organisa[tion]
promoting the use an[d]
preservation of aerial phot[ography]

The Care and Storage

of Photographs

Recommendations for good practice

David Wilson
Curator in aerial photography
University of Cambridge

First issued 1997
©Honorary Secretary NAPLIB

British Library Cataloguing in Publication Data
A Catalogue record for this book is available from the British Library
Published by NAPLIB

ISBN 0 9530436 0 6

Acknowledgments
The advice contained has been compiled mainly from the literature cited in the bibliography. The author is grateful to Tony Rumsey for the notes that formed a first draft of Chapter 3 and to David List and other fellow members of the Executive Committee of NAPLIB for constructive criticism of his text at all stages of its progress. The author is grateful to the following individuals and organisations for their assistance on the draft text: Ron Brooker and Hilary Roberts of the Imperial War Museum, Photograph Archive; Marke Browne and Sarah Jenner of The British Library Conservation Department; Stephen Harwood, David Parker and Peter Webb of the Public Record Office, Conservation Department.

Jacket illustration: Plotting and mounting on outline map cover the latest mosaic of aerial photographs in a Royal Flying Corps office near Arras, 1918 February 22. *Photograph by Official War Office Photographer Temporary Second Lieutenant David McClellan, Royal Flying Corps attached Photographic Section, GHQ, BEF, France.* McClellan, a press photographer for the *Daily Mirror* before the war became the Imperial War Museum photographer at its inception and later returned to Press photography. Many of his original negatives (Including that for this image) are still cared for to this day by the Imperial War Museum in London. (IWM Q8533)

Publication design and layout by Simon Shuel, 13 Woodberry Crescent, LONDON N10 1PJ

Contents

I Introduction

Aerial photographs may be taken for a great variety of purposes, but all are potentially of archival value.

It is the principal aim of NAPLIB *'to ensure the preservation of the greatest number of aerial photographs of the United Kingdom'*. If they are not stored in appropriate conditions, however, prints are liable to curling, fading, physical damage and fungal attack, while negatives may develop distortions, blistering and eventual degradation or loss of image. These effects can be experienced in a domestic environment, where they will be familiar to many, but the dangers are intensified in conditions of bulk storage.

It is thus fitting for NAPLIB to offer some guidance on the storage of aerial photographs. While it would be unrealistic to expect every small collection to adopt measures that we should regard as obligatory in a national archive, it still seems best to describe the dangers and appropriate precautions in full, in plain language, to inform and assist individuals when considering how far they ought to go. Commonsense decisions can then be made within a framework of understanding and of up-to-date information.

While the advice in this work is directed specifically at those responsible for the management of aerial photography collections, it is in fact applicable quite generally to non-specialist photographs taken since 1920 using standard techniques. There appears to be no comparable summary of these matters currently available, and NAPLIB would be only too pleased if the present work were to be found useful by a broad readership.

The dangers

In broad terms there are five dangers against which photographs need to be protected:
- theft
- fire
- water
- mechanical damage
- poor environmental conditions.

At first sight theft and fire are the worst perils, seeing that they can lead to total loss or destruction of the collection, but it should also be recognised that poor environmental conditions, if less sudden and dramatic in their operation, are no less devastating in their effect. The reactions between photographic materials and their environment are subtle and complex and potentially disastrous, so they naturally provoke much of the detailed advice contained within this work; but it is essential that every one of the dangers listed above is carefully assessed, both individually and in combination.

In devising effective countermeasures thought should be given to their possible interaction with each other. Thus, a security system designed to prevent photographs being stolen is more than likely to impede their legitimate removal in an emergency, if threatened by fire, flood or structural collapse.

Water damage is liable to occur in one of two contexts:
• leaks from tanks, pipes and radiators
• control and prevention of fire.

Of course, if the water supply and heating systems are properly maintained, there should be no trouble from leaks. Nevertheless, anyone who places a photo library or negative store in a room lying directly below the building's main water tanks or toilets is clearly asking for trouble. Similarly, cellars and basements should be avoided, if at all possible. In the case of actual fire, water damage must be judged the lesser evil and unavoidable. This simply underlines the need to avoid fires in the first place. But suppose an automatic sprinkler to be set off by accident, how well would storage cabinets and boxes resist the ensuing downpour?

Individual negatives or strips of negatives need to be protected from accidental scratching and abrasion by being placed in envelopes or files. At the same time it is vital that any materials in contact with the negatives do not set off, or accelerate, damaging chemical reactions; so great care should be taken in the design and specification of storage systems.

Photographs old and new

Individual collections will contain photographs of differing ages and processes in varying proportions.

Photographs from the early days of photography present a number of problems. They are often made of materials now obsolete, using processes that are outmoded and unfamiliar, and usually there is not even a record of what these processes were. Yet if the materials can be correctly identified, a good deal is now known about their behaviour when kept in various conditions, so it is not too difficult to prescribe a suitable environment for their long-term storage.

For new photographs it is just the opposite. We know how they have been made, but if the materials have been introduced at all recently, we know next to nothing about how they will last, even in the short term. Our response should therefore be cautious.

There are two ways to limit the risks:
• insist that the processing of all new photographs received is carried out to the highest standards, so that negatives and prints entering the collection are as far as possible chemically inert (see Appendix A).
• take care not to assume that the new materials currently in use are any longer lasting than the old ones, until such time as this is proved by experience. Until then, the environmental conditions prescribed for early photographs should be applied equally to those newly made.

Recommendations

Detailed recommendations for archivally sound storage of aerial photographs are given in succeeding chapters.

First of all, the dangers are reviewed in greater detail, noting for each both the effects of exposure to the particular danger and the means of protection against it.

The aim is to identify general principles more than to prescribe specific solutions, but the differing requirements of negatives and prints, black and-white and colour photographs will be separately treated in the course of Chapters 3-6.

For fuller details on all these topics reference should be made to the publications cited in Chapter 8.

Remedial action to counter the effects of fire, water and chemical damage, where this is possible, is a subject that lies outside the scope of this work. You may have received faded, stained or damaged prints from elsewhere, or your existing collection may have suffered some catastrophe: in either case you should seek the advice of a qualified photographic conservator. For useful addresses see Appendix C, or refer to the Society of Archivists' Directory of Suppliers, as described in Appendix B.

2   The dangers, and what can be done about them

Theft

No detailed advice is offered here about theft and how to prevent it, but this does not mean that the question is unimportant or should be neglected. It is simply that the problem is a very general one, not much related to the nature of photographs as such, and therefore it is largely omitted from this work.

No-one is very likely to attempt to steal a collection of photographs en masse, but individual prints or groups of prints are obviously vulnerable to theft by those who do not wish to pay for copies, and negatives might be purloined to prevent their use in legal proceedings; so appropriate precautions certainly need to be taken. These will depend on the organisation and staffing of the collection concerned; in general terms, the procedures for managing visitors to the collection should not present such visitors with an obvious opportunity for pilfering, and staff should be constantly, even conspicuously, vigilant.

Management procedures should also be in place to detect and prevent pilferage by staff, for no matter how trusted they may be, it should never be forgotten that the internal thief can cause greater undetected loss over a longer period than can any visitor.

Fire

The effect of fire on photographs

When photographic prints are exposed to flame, they burn readily and are quickly destroyed. Glass plates shatter. Modern photographic safety film (cellulose acetate or polyester) is designed to burn only with difficulty, but it will still do so if exposure to fire is prolonged; the burning is accompanied by emission of noxious fumes. Cellulose nitrate film is a notorious fire risk, capable of igniting at temperatures as low as $50°C/122°F$, or even $38°C/100°F$ when kept in a sealed container. When burning, it requires no oxygen from any other source and cannot be extinguished by water or carbon dioxide. A small quantity of film will produce enormous clouds of smoke and of severely toxic nitrogen dioxide, which, if inhaled, causes rapid and severe damage to the deep lung tissues (lung oedema).

When photographs are protected from actual flame, they may still be damaged or made unusable by exposure to heat. In photographs with a silver-gelatin image the quality of the image is little altered by exposure to temperatures as high as $66°C/150°F$, even over several hours, but dye images, as found in most colour photographs, can be expected to show some fading or change in colour balance. Thermally processed silver images will suffer degradation at temperatures above $50°C/120°F$. Both films and prints may nevertheless become so distorted that they are of no value for measurement and indeed can be viewed, printed or copied only with difficulty. In addition, overlapping sections of film or groups of prints may become stuck together by softened gelatin in the emulsion.

A further hazard is that plastic containers or enclosures such as negative sleeves may melt at high temperatures. Polyethylene (polythene) is particularly unsatisfactory, as it has a low melting-point, fuses to the photograph and is then quite irremovable.

As in many other contexts, the most damaging effect of a fire will often be the water used to put it out. The effect of water on photographs, and how best to protect them from such damage, is the subject of a later section.

Protection against fire
The best protection against fire is not to have one in the first place, or (failing that) to have an adequate warning system that allows the fire to be tackled before it becomes established.

Normal fire precautions should obviously be taken. Before the premises are taken into use, all wiring and electrical installations should be checked for safety by a qualified electrician, and all subsequent installations should be similarly checked. The same goes for heating systems. There should be no smoking anywhere on the premises, including the toilets, whether they are open to the public or not. If the smoking ban can be extended to all other parts of the building, so much the better.

Cellulose nitrate film should be kept in a separate fireproof store, away from all other negatives. Film of this type (see below, p 12) is a known fire risk of which account should be taken in the insurance policy for the building and its contents. If the policy contains a clause forbidding the storage of highly flammable material, the presence of nitrate film will invalidate it. In any case, such film is a dangerous substance about which both the insurers and the Fire Brigade are entitled to be informed before a fire actually occurs.

The conventional way to provide round-the-clock protection against fires developing is to fit an automatic system using smoke detectors, fire alarms and water sprinklers. Water sprinklers are effective in controlling fires, but they are also likely to cause damage to stored photographs; nevertheless it is better to have some photographs damaged by water than to have all of them destroyed by fire. In a modern sprinker-system only those sprinkler-heads nearest the fire actually go off, triggered by the local rise in temperature and they close themselves down if the fire is extinguished. A signal is passed automatically to the fire station, so even if the sprinkler operates by accident when nobody is there, the Fire and Rescue Service will still arrive and flooding will be averted. Halon gases, once regarded as a safe and effective alternative to water, are no longer approved because of their contribution to the greenhouse effect.

All shelving, cabinets and other fixtures and fittings in the store should be non-combustible. Storage boxes of plastic should be avoided as far as possible, even when these are chemically inert, and especially if the material has a low melting-point.

If there are relatively few photographs and they are regarded as having high value, it is possible to put them in insulated record containers.

According to recognised standards (see ISO 5466:1992) these should not attain an interior temperature greater than 60°C/140°F or interior relative humidity greater than 85 per cent during standard site fire exposure tests. Insulated record containers are preferable to fire-resisting safes, especially if these rely on generating steam to resist high temperature. Photographs stored in such a safe would need to be protected against the steam; otherwise there would be severe distortion, with melting of the emulsion.

5

For full protection against fire and associated hazards film should be placed in closed containers, and prints in enclosures, in either fire-resistant vaults or insulated record containers. The latter should be placed on a ground-supported floor unless the building itself is fire-resistant. The term 'ground-supported' is quoted direct from the relevant International Standard and presumably means a solid floor at the lowest level of the building, ie at ground level unless there is a basement. The material of any enclosures around the photographs should be able to withstand heating to 150°C/302°F for four hours without igniting and without releasing more fumes than the film itself does. If the material melts or distorts at such a temperature, it will be important that this does not damage the photograph or prevent it being removed from the enclosure thereafter.

We have already noted that polythene is particularly unsatisfactory in these respects; the performance of other materials should be checked with the manufacturer, if this method of storage is adopted.

In practice, most collections of aerial photographs are too numerous for their storage in insulated record containers to be a realistic proposition, so that protective measures will be limited to the prevention and control of fire, as described above.

Ultimately, the most effective, though expensive, safeguard against loss of archival material through fire is to make duplicate copies and to keep them in another building.

Water

The effect of water on photographs
The effect of water on photographs, whether the result of fire control or of accidental flooding, is like that of high relative humidity raised to the nth degree. Overlapping prints or sections of film will become stuck together by gelatin in the emulsion and in the backing layer (if present). If these are not carefully separated and then dried within 48 hours of being soaked, there is a strong possibility of mould beginning to grow on the emulsion. Discolouration and fading of the image may also be initiated. The effect of spilt drinks or other fluids is even more devastating, resulting in stains, stickiness and unwanted chemical reactions.

Protection against water
The print library and negative store should be sited away from obvious risk of leaking water and flooding. A purpose-designed storage area will not only be sited out of danger from tanks and cisterns, as noted above; it will have no water-pipes whatever running above or beside it. Cellars and basements should likewise be avoided. If basement storage is unavoidable, cabinets should be raised on high plinths, and sumps should be set in the floor, with pumps fitted to extract unwanted water.

The main precaution against water damage is to keep photographs in closed cabinets and containers. These will seldom be actually sealed, but they should never be left with doors, drawers or lids open. The upper surfaces of cabinets should contain no vents or holes through which water could penetrate; side vents should be designed to exclude and throw off water; and doors and the fronts of drawers should fit flush, with no protruding flanges to guide trickling water into the interior. By these simple expedients major damage from water flows can be avoided. Relative humidity of the atmosphere will nevertheless be increased to an unacceptable level and should be brought under control without delay.

As to other fluids, such as hot or cold drinks, cosmetics, correcting fluid and so on, these should never be allowed in close proximity to photographs and should never be placed on the same work-surface.

Mechanical damage

The effect of mechanical damage on photographs
Mechanical damage to the emulsion of a photograph removes or obscures part of the image and so reduces its value as a source of information.

The commonest forms of damage are scratching and other acts of abrasion. Folding and creasing cause local distortion; moreover, since it is difficult to restore a well-creased photograph to perfect flatness, they also inhibit accurate measurement and reproduction. All papers and most films are to a greater or less degree susceptible to tearing.

Protection against mechanical damage
Photographs are placed in a variety of enclosures and containers, both to protect them from mechanical damage and from other dangers, such as dust and light, and also for ease of access in accordance with the collection's filing system. We have already seen that they should be resistant to high temperature, and that containers and cabinets should exclude water.

These protective devices introduce a secondary danger, not of mechanical but of chemical damage. The necessary sleeves, envelopes, folders, files, boxes, cans and housings all need to be made of materials that will neither cause nor accelerate harmful chemical reactions in the photographs. This is especially important for enclosures which come into actual contact with photographs. While the design of enclosures will be specific to the types of photographs enclosed, and further comments on this will be found in Chapters 3-6 below, the materials of which they are made can be reviewed in more general terms, which is done here. (Containers are considered below in company with shelves and other fittings.)

The material used in making an enclosure is of vital importance for the safekeeping of the photograph and the permanence of its image. Choosing the right one is no simple matter.

Recommended materials include the following, always provided that they contain no additives:
- polyethylene terephthalate sheeting without surface coating (eg, Dupont Mylar D or ICI Melinex 516)
- polypropylene sheeting without surface coating (eg, Hercules T500 film)
- cellulose triacetate sheeting without surface coating and not containing more than 15 parts of plasticizer per 100 parts of ester
- high grade paper or board of conservation quality with a smooth surface (eg, Atlantis Silversafe Photostore).

The latter should be high in alpha-cellulose (over 87%), lignin-free, made from rag, bleached sulphite or bleached kraft pulp, and non-buffered, i.e. pH-neutral (pH 7.0-7.5) rather than simply 'acid-free'. It should contain no waxes, plasticisers, or other ingredients that might transfer to the emulsion, and there should be minimum sizing, using only chemicals that are neutral or alkaline.

Materials to be avoided include the following:
- chlorinated or nitrated plastic sheeting, including polyvinyl chloride (PVC)
- highly plasticised sheeting, including most cellulose acetates
- plastics with residual solvents or plasticisers
- polyethylene (polythene), especially when of low density
- surface-coated polypropylene
- matte polyester (eg, Dupont Mylar EB-11)
- plastics of undeclared composition
- glassine, either conventional or acid-free
- kraft paper or low-grade paper or board that does not meet the specification given above
- synthetic paper-like materials (eg, Dupont Tyvek).

Enclosures should be constructed as far as possible without the use of adhesive. Where adhesive is required, wheat starch paste is suitable for use with paper. Other adhesives should be avoided, especially those that are hygroscopic, or contain iron, copper or sulphur impurities, and rubber cement. Pressure-sensitive tapes (eg, masking and drafting tape) and ether-linked materials should also be avoided.

For enclosures made of materials other than plastic the Photographic Activity Test developed by the American National Standards Institute has now been adopted by the International Organization for Standardization (see ISO 10214) and presumably the British Standards Institution will follow. This test, carried out in a professional laboratory, guarantees that the material used contains no chemicals harmful to a black-and-white photographic emulsion, even when the two remain in continuous contact. (Unfortunately, the test is not reliable for plastic materials or in relation to colour emulsions.)

Many products that are marketed for the storage of photographs do not fully meet the standards outlined above. Suppliers should be closely questioned about the materials used in their products. It is not enough to be assured that the plastic used is 'safe': what in fact is its composition?

Some suppliers of enclosures and containers of genuine conservation quality are listed in Appendix B.

Poor environmental conditions

The areas of concern are temperature, relative humidity, air purity and light.

The effect of extremes of temperature and relative humidity on photographs

Temperature and relative humidity (RH) must inevitably be considered together because RH is a measure of the amount of water contained in the air compared with the maximum amount the same air could hold at the particular temperature then prevailing. Raising temperature increases the air's capacity to hold water and so acts to reduce RH, whereas lowering temperature has the opposite effect and increases RH.

Temperature is mainly important for its effect on RH, but it is also a major control on the rate of chemical degradation of photographs. With organic materials capable of absorbing water each rise in temperature of 10°C/18°F roughly doubles the rate of chemical reaction.

High relative humidity (eg, over 60 per cent) has a whole range of undesirable effects. It softens gelatine in the emulsion layer - and in the backing layer of gelatin-backed films - which is then receptive to the growth of mould. Mites and larger insects may then feed on the mould or on the gelatin itself. The emulsion layer can display ferrotyping (turning glossy where it is pressed against a smooth surface) or in extreme conditions become stuck to other surfaces, such as filing envelopes, overlapping film or prints. Any residual hypo (thiosulphate) will react with grains of metallic silver in the image to produce discolouration and fading. Finally, hydrolysis initiates chemical degradation of the base of certain types of film (discussed in greater detail in Chapter 3).

Low relative humidity (eg, below 25 per cent), especially when associated with high temperature, dries out the emulsion layer and leads to brittleness in both films and paper.

It should be borne in mind that the fluctuation or cycling of temperature and RH is particularly destructive and should be avoided. Regular cycling of temperature and RH on a daily basis (eg, if the store is lit by incandescent lamps during working hours but not otherwise) is worst of all.

Protection against extremes of temperature and relative humidity

The well-being of stored photographs normally requires them to be kept in conditions combining a moderate temperature with moderate RH. The figures appropriate to different kinds of photographs are specified below in Chapters 3-6. Temperature should not be allowed to fluctuate by more than 4°C/7°F, nor RH by more than 5 per cent.

The same rule applies here as to the storage of wine: it is better to go for a value that can be maintained without variation, even if it is relatively high in the acceptable range, than to strive vainly for some ideal value that cannot actually be guaranteed. Within obvious limits, consistency is more important than absolute value.

It could be argued that a low temperature (eg, below 10°C/50°F) would be ideal for the storage of photographs, if it were not for the practical problems that go with it. Special care would need to be taken at such a temperature to keep RH within acceptable limits. In addition, since a low-temperature store does not provide a suitable working environment, if any of the photographs were to be put to actual use, they would have to be temporarily transferred to somewhere less chilly. Such a change of conditions is itself harmful and this could outweigh the beneficial effects of cool-storage. Nevertheless, low-temperature storage is recommended for colour photographs and is described further in Chapter 5, below.

Fortunately, in the temperate zone there should be little difficulty in maintaining moderate temperature and RH without resort to air-conditioning and humidity controls, but this should not be taken for granted. Temperature and RH should be assessed when designing the store and monitored thereafter.

It is important to allow air to circulate freely throughout the store, as stagnant air favours fungal and insect infestation. Cabinets and containers should not stand so close to the walls and to each other that air does not regularly pass behind and between them. There should be no carpets or curtains or other textiles fitted.

Where air-conditioning does have to be provided, this should operate constantly, not merely during working hours, and special attention should be given to RH, as dehumidification is likely to be needed also. This should be achieved with proper dehumidification equipment, not by introducing desiccating agents into the storage area. There should be slight positive air pressure. All equipment should be subject to an automatic control system responding to check thermometers and humidity indicators.

If the air does need to be dehumidified, it is essential to remember that this will have no effect inside any closed containers, unless these are provided with vents in their sides. Air trapped inside cans of roll film, for example, will continue at the same humidity as prevailed when the lid was last put on. So, if the temperature in the store is subsequently reduced, the RH inside each can is bound to rise - even if air circulating in the store is dehumidified - unless the lid is also lifted. If the films (or other photographs) are vacuum-packed in sealed containers, this will no longer be a problem, but this method is only appropriate to long-term storage where no access is required.

The effect of contaminated air on photographs
Air in the photograph store may be contaminated by dust and by harmful gases.

Solid particles of dust falling on photographs will eventually give rise to scratching or other forms of physical damage. If the dust is chemically reactive, fading or staining of the image may result.

More insidious is the presence of harmful gases in the atmosphere, especially those liable to cause oxidation of the silver image. These include ozone, peroxides, sulphur dioxide, hydrogen sulphide, nitric oxide, nitrogen dioxide, formaldehydes, chlorine and ammonia. Even quite small concentrations can produce rapid fading and staining.

Protection against contaminated air
Immediate protection against dust is normally by means of enclosures - the same envelopes, sleeves, folders or files that give protection against mechanical damage, with the same restrictions on the materials from which they are made . An outer defence is offered by the container in which the sleeved photographs are kept.

If the store has an air supply, this should incorporate mechanical filters, preferably of dry-media type having an arrestance rating of not less than 85 per cent in standard tests. The filters should be of the non-combustible variety (see ISO 5466:1992).

The need to exclude harmful gases from the store may affect the siting of the photographic collection itself within the landscape, the location of the store within the building, and the use of equipment in or near the store. This means that it makes no sense to establish a photographic archive in a seaside location (high in ozone), or in an industrial area, especially if that industry involves burning of fossil fuels (yielding sulphur dioxide). The store should not be close to petrol or diesel engines, oil- or gas-fired boilers, or electrostatic photocopiers (which give off ozone). If there is an air-conditioning system, attention should be paid to the air intakes: these should not be placed where there is any possibility of sucking in chemical fumes or dry chemicals. Chemical fumes in this context include those given off by paints, lacquers and varnishes less than three months old. Within the store, shelves, cabinets and other fittings should not be of wood, chipboard, hardboard or similar natural materials, because these (whether painted or varnished or not) give off peroxides over time which will fade the silver image. The most suitable materials are:
- anodized aluminium
- stainless steel
- steel with baked-on non-plasticised synthetic resin lacquer
- inert and impermeable plastics, such as polypropylene or cellulose acetate.

Finishes containing natural, acrylic, chlorinated or highly plasticised resins can all be harmful. Rubber should also be avoided. Harmful chemicals, including normal household cleaners containing chlorine or ammonia, should on no account be introduced into the storage area. It should also be noted that decomposing film (see Chapter 3) can give off gases that affect the image on other photographs. Gaseous impurities can be removed from the air by suitable washers and absorbers, using treated water to eliminate sulphur dioxide and activated carbon to absorb sulphur dioxide and hydrogen sulphide. (Hydrogen sulphide is a rare contaminant, though very active even at low concentrations; it can nevertheless occur even in the actual air-washer, if this contains decomposed biological slime.) Air-washers require consistent control and, in the case of activated carbon, expert processing.

The effect of light on photographs
Direct sunlight and light derived from some other sources (including most fluorescent lamps) contain a high level of ultraviolet (UV) radiation. This stimulates several forms of degradation:
- staining and fading of the silver image, especially in poorly processed photographs
- fading of the dyes in colour photographs
- damage to cellulose in photographic paper.

Protection against light
All photographs are best kept in the dark.

The first line of defence is to keep all photographs inside reasonably light-tight storage boxes, cans, drawers and cabinets. Lighting in the stores should be subdued and certainly no brighter than is strictly necessary for efficient operation. Light sources with a high level of UV radiation should not be used.

The ideal store has no outside windows. If windows are present, direct sunlight can be excluded with dark blinds or rendered harmless with UV filters (specially designed plastic sheeting stuck directly to the panes). The effectiveness of the measures can be checked with a UV light monitor. UV filters should be checked regularly (at least every five years) for peeling and for mechanical damage.

Artificial lighting should also be, as far as possible, UV-free. Incandescent lamps meet this requirement but exact a price for it by generating a significant amount of heat. As long as illumination is kept to a modest level, however, the amount of heat produced should not cause a problem. The alternative is to use special fluorescent lamps incorporating a UV filter.

The special requirements of prints that have to be made available for study are discussed further in Chapter 4.

3 Storing processed black-and-white film and plates

NB. The contents of this chapter apply equally to negatives and diapositives, but for simplicity the term 'negative' is used throughout.

Identifying which sort of film or plate

Negatives may be on glass plates or on film.

Glass plates
Although popular in France for aerial survey because of their excellent dimensional stability, glass plates have seldom been used in Britain for this purpose. This is because of the great practical disadvantages of bulk, weight and fragility. Glass plates were nevertheless the standard for serious general photography between the two World Wars and many early aerial photographs will have been taken on them, like the pioneering archaeological photography of O. G. S. Crawford and A. Keiller in 1924 (published in their classic book *Wessex from the Air*).

Photographic plates are of several kinds, according to the composition of the light-sensitive coating. The only kind likely to be encountered in a collection of aerial photographs is the gelatin dry plate, and comment will be limited to this.

If glass plates are present, it would be worth considering whether to copy them onto film as a precaution against damage. The copy will inevitably lose something by comparison with an intact original, but it will be vastly more informative than a plate that has been accidentally shattered.

Film
It is necessary to distinguish between photographic films of three broad types: cellulose nitrate, cellulose acetate, and polyester. All normally carry a gelatin/silver emulsion.

Cellulose nitrate film has good dimensional stability but poor archival quality; it is also highly flammable. Cellulose acetate was introduced in the 1930s as a safer replacement, but early formulations suffered from shrinkage and from brittleness in dry conditions. It was not until the late 1940s that cellulose triacetate film became established as a viable alternative, and production of cellulose nitrate ceased c.1950. Various polyester films were introduced a decade later; these are exceptionally strong and tough, with very low water absorption and improved dimensional stability. Today, films designed for survey (topographic films) are normally of polyester, while those designed for general purposes are of cellulose triacetate.

Cellulose nitrate. - This is dimensionally stable but decomposes over time. This decomposition is irreversible, proceeds slowly for some decades, but then accelerates. The rate of decomposition increases if the gases formed (nitric oxide and nitrogen dioxide) are unable to escape from the cans or other containers holding the film, and also when there is high temperature and high relative humidity. The film is highly flammable and, when decomposition is advanced, may ignite spontaneously. It can also ignite when exposed to temperatures as low as 50°C/122°F (See Chapter 2). Nevertheless, if kept at recommended levels of temperature and relative humidity, intact nitrate film is as safe as any other.

Cellulose nitrate film can be distinguished from modern safety films by two tests:
- it burns readily when exposed to a flame
- it sinks in trichloroethylene.

For the burning test cut a sliver of film from the edge of the negative (say, 3 x 250 mm); hold it vertically with tweezers or pliers at the lower end over an ashtray and ignite it at the top. Nitrate film will burn quickly and strongly downwards with a bright yellow flame until the whole sample is consumed. Safety film will ignite with difficulty and will generally go out soon after the flame is removed. This test should obviously not be attempted close to any other film or other kinds of flammable material.

For the flotation test a small piece of film about 5 mm square is placed in a clear glass container containing trichloroethylene. Stop the mouth of the container and shake it to ensure that the sample is completely wetted. If it then sinks, it is cellulose nitrate; if it floats, it is safety film. Trichloroethylene can be obtained from specialist suppliers of laboratory chemicals; care should be taken to follow recommended safety precautions, especially not to inhale the fumes. (See *Health and Safety Commission, Guidance Note EH 40/89, Occupational Exposure Limits 1989*).

This type of film continued to be manufactured and used until c.1950, when it was wholly replaced by cellulose triacetate, so all surviving specimens will be over 45 years old and highly suspect. They should be kept away from the rest of the negatives in a cool, dry and fireproof place and inspected regularly for deterioration. Copies should be made onto safety film and the originals destroyed as soon as decomposition is certainly detected. (This should be done with great care, in an open place, a small quantity at any one time, preferably by the Fire Brigade.)

The visible symptoms of decomposition are brittleness, buckling, yellowing of the film base, softening of the gelatin and oxidation of the silver image. If the film is brittle enough to crack when folded, it has already started to decompose. Another test is to cut off a small strip, soak in water for one minute, and then scrape off the emulsion; if the base so exposed is seen to be yellowing (eg, by contrast with a piece of white paper), then again decomposition has started. If the photographic image itself is seen to be breaking down, handle with extreme care: decomposition is far advanced and the negatives should be destroyed immediately.

Cellulose acetate. - While not as spectacularly impermanent as cellulose nitrate, cellulose acetates are also subject to irreversible deterioration. Their life can, however, be extended by correct storage conditions paying particular attention to relative humidity.

Cellulose acetate films can be distinguished from cellulose nitrate by two tests:
- they burn only with difficulty
- they float in trichloroethylene.

They can be distinguished from polyesters by the fact that they can be easily torn.

Polyester. - Examples are polycarbonate and polyethylene terephthalate. The latter has exceptional strength and stiffness. The actual polyester base is resistant to changes induced by extremes of temperature and humidity, but this does not apply to the emulsion layer, which may thus lift from the base in extreme conditions.

Polyesters can be distinguished from cellulose nitrate by the same tests as described above for cellulose acetate. They can be distinguished from cellulose acetates by the fact that they can only be torn with difficulty.

Processing negatives for maximum stability

Conventional processing, if done with due care, should ensure permanence for several decades. Thereafter, even very modest traces of processing chemicals retained on the negative will inevitably contribute to its eventual deterioration. A longer life can only be achieved by taking special trouble to remove the unwanted chemicals completely. The relevant procedures are set out in Appendix A. This sequence greatly extends the time taken in processing, but it also extends the life of the silver image to the point where survival depends primarily on the nature and condition of the base, viz. the glass plate or film bearing the emulsion.

It is obvious that, as far as possible, a curator should seek to ensure that any new negatives entering the collection for which he or she is responsible have been processed to this special standard.

Handling negatives

No one should ever touch the emulsion. Even the lightest touch of a finger transfers greasy moisture that will start a chemical reaction and eventually become visible as an obvious mark. When negatives have to be handled, they should be held by the edges.

In addition, those handling negatives should avoid using hand cream or hand lotions and should wash after contact with any oil or greasy substance. (This may include their own hair.) It is best to wear lint-free cotton gloves, but these must be kept clean and free of grit and should be replaced before they become badly worn.

Storing negatives

Provided negatives have received scrupulous processing and are handled correctly, the factors that affect their permanence are the environmental conditions in the store (temperature, relative humidity and air purity) and the materials of any enclosures or containers with which they come into contact.

Temperature and relative humidity
Extremes of temperature and relative humidity (RH) should be avoided (Chapter 2). Correct RH in particular is critical.

High temperature (eg, 27°C/80°F) in a dry atmosphere dries out the emulsion layer, causing shrinkage and distortion of the image. The emulsion layer also tends to develop an electrostatic charge, attracting dust particles to the surface. In a moist atmosphere high temperature intensifies and accelerates chemical reactions and other troubles fostered by high RH. Overheating increases the fire risk of nitrate films. Low temperature (eg, below 10°C/50°F) apart from causing temporary brittleness in film below 0°C/32°F, is not in itself hazardous to photographic materials and may even be regarded as favourable, but special care is needed at such temperatures to keep RH within acceptable limits.

High relative humidity (eg, over 60 per cent) has a whole range of undesirable effects.

It softens gelatin in the emulsion layer - and in the backing layer of gelatin-backed films - which is then open to biological attack. The emulsion layer can display ferrotyping (turning glossy where it is pressed against overlapping film) or even become stuck to other surfaces, such as filing envelopes or overlapping film. Any residual hypo (thiosulphate) will react with grains of metallic silver in the image to produce discolouration and fading.

Hydrolysis initiates the chemical degradation of the film base. Nitrate films release nitric oxide and nitrogen dioxide. This leads to yellowing of the base, fading of the image and eventual disintegration of the base, culminating in spontaneous combustion. With acetate films acetic acid is released, and this in turn allows plasticisers (normally present in modern films) to crystallize on the film surface in a white deposit. Tensile strength is lost and the film becomes brittle; circular patterns of bubbles are found between the base and the emulsion layer; and shrinkage occurs, causing separation of the emulsion from the base.

Low relative humidity (eg, below 25 per cent) causes a temporary increase in film curl and brittleness. Negatives stored at low RH would need careful reconditioning before use in the darkroom. Prolonged exposure to very low RH also causes shrinkage and distortion in the emulsion layer. This is particularly unwelcome on an unyielding glass plate but is little better on a polyester base, which is also designed to be resistant to physical change in extreme conditions. The emulsion tends to lift from the base; typical symptoms are peeling at edges, flaking, cracking and frilling of the emulsion.

Recommended values for temperature and RH are as follows.

- Glass plates . . . . .up to 20°C/68°F   20-50 per cent
- Nitrate films . . . . .10°C/50°F   not above 45 per cent
- Acetate films . . . . .up to 21°C/70°F   15-50 per cent
- If gelatine-backed . . . . .up to 21°C/70°F   25-50 per cent
- Polyester films . . . . .up to 21°C/70°F   30-50 per cent

Where a range is given, lower values are appropriate for long-term archival storage, higher values for holding negatives in common use. Temperature should not be allowed to fluctuate by more than 4°C/7°F, nor RH by more than 5 per cent, and regular cycling of temperature and RH on a daily basis must be avoided at all costs.

The need to avoid fluctuation in environmental conditions is not limited to the negative store. If negatives in a collection are still being used for making prints, they will occasionally have to go into the darkroom. To avoid the possibly harmful effect of such a transfer, it is desirable for the conditions in both areas to be similar. For practical reasons, this is likely to mean that RH in the negative store will need to be close to 50 per cent. As to temperature, differences cause most trouble in relation to glass plates, which are capable of retaining their original temperature in a changed environment for a considerable period. If plates are held at a storage temperature below the dew point of the air in the darkroom, there is likely to be condensation of moisture on their surfaces at the time of transfer, unless they have previously been placed in a container and unless the container and its contents are then brought to room temperature before opening. (This might take several hours.)

Air purity
Air in the negative store should be free of dust and of harmful gases, whether introduced from outside or produced in the store itself (Chapter 2).

A specific hazard is that decomposing cellulose nitrate film gives off gases (nitric oxide and nitrogen dioxide) that not only accelerate its own degradation but also affect the image on cellulose acetate films. It is therefore inadvisable (quite apart from the fire risk) to store nitrate and other films either together in the same room or in rooms connected by ventilating ducts.

Enclosures and containers
General advice has been given above on the design and material of enclosures and containers with respect to fire prevention , protection against water flows , minimizing chemical degradation, and ensuring favourable environmental conditions (Chapter 2).

The following comments are specific to the needs of plates and film.

It should never be forgotten that both nitrate and acetate films do have a limited life and will deteriorate in the end. When negatives are kept in enclosures of inappropriate materials, this deterioration will occur sooner, or be more severe, or take effect in some places in preference to others, causing unsightly local fading or staining.

Glass plates should not be stored horizontally, or stacked on one another, or with emulsion surfaces in contact. Individual plates should be placed in their own sleeves, envelopes or folders and stored standing on the longer edge in specially designed containers, cabinets or other storage housings. These will be specific to the size of the plate; recommended designs are described in BS ISO 3897:1992.

Cut film should be kept flat, by holding it firmly between stiff supports. A rigid cardboard box of suitable quality, if filled with negatives, would give sufficient support even when stored on edge; but if only half full, it would fail to do so. The individual pieces of film should be separated and protected by their own sleeves, envelopes or folders, or by the pockets of a filing system. Nitrate film should be stored in paper enclosures, not plastic.

Enclosures should be designed so as to avoid the likelihood of scratching during insertion of the negative and so as not to place uneven pressure on its surface. Seams should therefore be at the side, not up the middle. If a seam does have to cross the face of a negative, this should be stored with the emulsion layer facing away from the seam. It is an advantage if the material of the enclosure is transparent, so that preliminary examination of the negative can take place without having to remove one from the other.

A commonly used enclosure for glass plates is the four-flap paper enclosure. The plate is laid at the centre of the paper and four rectangular flaps, each the size of the plate, are folded over it in turn. No adhesive is used, and there is nothing to cause scratches.

Probably the most suitable form of enclosure, for glass plates as well as cut film, is an open-ended sleeve with overlapping top flap, made of transparent uncoated polyester, polypropylene or cellulose triacetate. The sleeves must be of just the right size and shape for each type of negative to be enclosed and the two folds needed in order to make it must be really tight, so that they clasp the negative effectively. Such a sleeve provides protection against finger prints and chemical contamination during routine handling and examination. To exclude dust the sleeved negative needs to be kept in a paper envelope of appropriate design. This should have narrow side seams (made by folding narrow side flaps over the body of the envelope and sticking them down on the outside), a folded seamless bottom, and an ungummed top flap. Up to ten sleeved negatives could be placed in a single envelope, according to need or preference. Reference numbers or other identification can be written, with care, on the outside. This should always be done without any negatives in the envelope to avoid any possibility of contact damage from the writing instrument.

Roll film is kept on its own spool upright inside a cylindrical can. There is contact between overlapping parts of the film, but the continuity of the film itself ensures that there is no contact between areas of emulsion in different parts. The film should be rolled tightly, but not under very great tension.

Roll films are commonly stored for convenience in the same cans in which the unprocessed film was originally supplied by the manufacturer. Up to c1975 these were made of tin-plated iron, thereafter of plastic. It is unfortunate that, as a result, the older films (which are most at risk) will be kept in the metal cans, seeing this actually contributes to the degradation of the negative base, at least in acetate films. Experimental results suggest that film stored in plastic cans is likely to survive for nearly twice as long (60 years estimated) as film in metal cans (35 years estimated).

The rolled film should not be held in place with rubber bands or pressure sensitive tape. If paper tape is used, it should be of conservation quality.

Increasing the longevity of stored negatives

Meticulous processing, correct environmental conditions and the use of conservation-quality enclosures all help to stave off premature deterioration of negatives in a photographic collection. Can any additional positive action be taken to extend their life ?

It is a grave mistake to apply any kind of lacquer (eg, diacetate) as a protective coating. Not only may this coating become discoloured itself; it will also accelerate degradation of the film by trapping the degradation products and not allowing them to escape into the environment.

A promising new development is the stabilizing bath, in which a combination of three stabilizers checks, or at least slows down, the degradation of both nitrate and acetate films by these means:
• scavenging nitric or acetic acid
• decomposing peroxides to safe products
• isolating metal ions so that they cannot participate in the degradative process.
This method has been proved in the laboratory (Allen et al, 1990), but awaits the results of practical trials before it is made generally available.

Inspecting stored negatives

A number of different representative samples of film should be inspected every two years. Nitrate film should be examined at least every year. The sampling programme should be prepared in advance and a different lot should be examined on each occasion. If it is known that the recommendations for temperature and relative humidity have not actually been observed, inspections should take place more frequently.

The purpose of inspection is to detect any physical changes in the film (curling, distortion, brittleness, stickiness, cracking, flaking or peeling of the emulsion), any visual changes in the film (fading, spotting or discolouration) and any changes in the material of enclosures (brittleness, discolouration). Visual inspection should be supplemented by consideration of unusual smells: decaying nitrate and acetate films both give off pungent odours (acetic acid smells like vinegar). If in doubt, make a closer visual examination.

Once the nature of any deterioration has been determined and its cause identified, action should be taken, where possible, to halt it or to put it right. Both the fault and the remedy should be recorded for future reference.

Cleaning negatives

It is possible to remove surface dirt, grease and mould from the emulsion of a negative with a special film cleaner solution, such as Kodak Film Cleaner or PEC-12® print cleaner (available from Process Supplies (London) Ltd, see Appendix C). This cannot reverse any damage already caused, but it may be able to remove, or at least to diminish, an unwanted blemish. Great care is called for. While it is not necessary to be a trained conservator, no one should undertake this task who is not used to handling film and does not understand its structure. No attempt should be made to clean a negative whose emulsion is lifting from the base.

Only the special film cleaner should be used. Other solvents may be harmful. If there has been fungal growth, it is particularly important not to allow water to come into contact with the emulsion, as this may have become water soluble. Even with film cleaner, a spot test should be made: with a microswab place a very small drop of the solvent on the margin of the negative (not on the actual image) and watch closely under oblique lighting, so as to show up any deformation of the surface of the emulsion; blot carefully after a few minutes or when a change begins to be seen. Assuming the spot-test to be satisfactory, the solvent may be applied a little at a time with light circular movements of a cotton swab, which is replaced as often as it becomes dirty. This is continued until the swab no longer picks up dirt and grease, and no streaks are left on the emulsion. Discarded cotton swabs should be placed in a resealable container and disposed of regularly and safely. The whole operation should be carried out in a very clean and well-ventilated area, ideally a fume cupboard, and the solvent container should be kept closed between applications.

Copying negatives

In the end, the only way to ensure the survival of a photographic image on cellulose nitrate or cellulose acetate film is to copy it before it deteriorates.

To avoid certain repetition of the same problem in future, it is prudent to use film with a polyester base. In other respects the film used should be matched to the characteristics of the original, to give faithful reproduction in terms of resolution, edge-sharpness and tonal range. Processing should obviously be of a kind to promote archival permanence.

4   Storing black-and-white prints

Prints as archival material

When the negatives are available, either in the same collection or in another, many prints are more or less expendable. They should be treated with care and respect, but they can still be replaced, when necessary, at the cost merely of some time and materials. Other prints may carry written details of processing, identification or provenance not present on the negatives and therefore of enduring significance. By contrast, when the relevant negatives are lost or damaged, all prints then become an irreplaceable archive and warrant curation to more exacting standards. At the same time, they must remain accessible for study or else they serve no purpose; it is no answer simply to withdraw archival prints from use in order to preserve them for posterity. Either copies must be made for everyday reference, so allowing archival prints to be kept undisturbed in a special store, or special arrangements will be needed to minimise the risks of mechanical damage and environmental stress during inspection and study.

The advice given here is for the storage specifically of archival prints. The paradox is that, at the time they are made, it is not normally foreseen that such prints are going to outlive their negatives and so no extra-special care is taken in the original printing. Aerial photographs, for the most part, are taken to meet some immediate need and not as a long-term record. They become outdated in five to ten years at most, and it is only later that their value as historic documents becomes increasingly evident. Obviously, prints that are consciously intended for an archive should be made using special procedures as noted below, but in reality very few aerial photographs will ever be printed to anything but the most ordinary standard.

Identifying which sort of paper

Positive images of aerial photographs are printed either on film as diapositives or on paper. The diapositives should be treated in the same way as negative film (Chapter 3, above). We are here concerned with paper prints.

There are two kinds of paper currently in use: fibre-base paper and resin-coated paper. The latter has now replaced earlier water-resistant ('waterproof') papers which were introduced for printing aerial photographs about 1940 to achieve greater dimensional stability. These were coated on both sides with a cellulose ester lacquer to inhibit water penetration, but this also made them somewhat more prone to curling and cracking.

Fibre-base paper. - This is the traditional photographic paper made of cellulose fibre, resistant to the action of photographic chemicals whether acid or alkaline, chemically inert with respect to the actual light-sensitive emulsion, and still remarkably strong when saturated with water. This paper has two main disadvantages: if chemicals penetrate between the fibres of the paper, they are not easily washed out; and the paper all too easily stretches or shrinks when wet or during drying.

Fibre-base paper can be readily distinguished from resin-coated paper by the fact that it will absorb water. (Place a small drop on the margin of the print and await developments.)

Resin-coated paper. - This is actually coated with polyethylene. There is very little penetration of the paper by chemicals, but when this does occur (by seepage from the edges), the chemicals are effectively trapped and are virtually impossible to wash out. There are other disadvantages. In low or fluctuating humidity the paper (unlike the emulsion layer) will not shrink, so encouraging the emulsion then to lift, with consequent cracking, peeling, flaking or rippling and inevitable distortion of the image. Furthermore, in the presence of light, polyethylene will sometimes react with titanium dioxide and other substances in the emulsion to produce discolouration. For these reasons resin-coated paper is not recommended for making prints to be kept in a long-term archive.

Ironically, when prints receive normal (rather than archival) processing, those on resin-coated paper are likely to fade less quickly than those on uncoated paper, because they needed less washing in the first place to remove unwanted chemical residues.

Resin-coated paper has a characteristic feel and appearance. Uncertainty in identification, however, may be resolved by the water drop test described above. It may also be noted that excessive heat, eg, in a film dryer, will cause blistering in resin-coated paper, where it would only cause curling in the traditional uncoated paper.

Processing prints for maximum stability

We have already seen that, in practice, prints of aerial photographs seldom receive special processing, but we should not make this an excuse for simply ignoring the established techniques for giving prints a longer life. Two alternative methods are described below in Appendix A. (Resin-coated paper is not recommended for archival prints, but if it is used, these special procedures should not be adopted.)

Storing prints

Temperature and relative humidity
Extremes of temperature and relative humidity (RH) should be avoided (Chapter 2). Temperature above 30°C/86°F will accelerate chemical reactions that degrade the image. Temperature below 0°C/32°F makes the gelatin emulsion brittle. RH above 60 per cent allows mould growth and accelerates the damaging effects of any residual chemicals (such as thiosulphate) in the emulsion. RH below 20 per cent produces temporary brittleness in gelatin emulsions and curling of prints.

Recommended values for temperature and RH are as follows:
- 15-18°C/59-64°F 30%-50%

Daily cycling of temperature should not exceed 4°C/7°F, and short-term cycling of

Thorpe Railway Station, Norwich, Norfolk on Jubilee Day 1897 June 22. Taken by the late Albert E. Coe of A. E. Coe and Sons, Photographers of London Street, Norwich, from a hot-air balloon launched from behind the Corn Hall.

Discovered in the records of the Colman and Rye Local Studies Library, Norwich in 1987 by Derek Edwards during research for the book *Wings over Norfolk: Early Aviation and the Pioneer Air Photographers,* the print from the original negative, possibly the earliest extant aerial photograph to be taken in the UK, was destroyed in the catastrophic fire which engulfed Norwich Central Library on 1994 August 1. Although much was recovered from the disaster this image survives only because the Local Studies Library consented to a short-term loan for a litho plate to be made for publication in the book: a case of preservation by exception if ever there was one! Colman and Rye Local Studies Library Photograph Reference NO-23249.

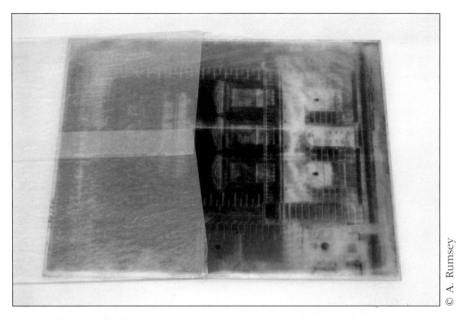

Plate 1: Glassine bags, even when acid-free, contain a plasticizer capable of harming the silver image. Here, glue from the central seam has also leaked out, causing further damage. See p 8.

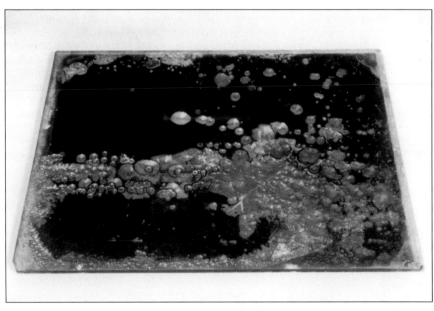

© A. Rumsey

Plate 3: Cellulose diacetate was an early safety film, but was subject to shrinkage from the loss of plasticizer over time, causing the emulsion to lift in a network pattern of covered 'channels'. See p 12.

Plate 2: Even glass plates, though generally very stable, will deteriorate in poor environmental conditions. Exfoliation of the surface on the emulsion side is here viewed from the other side through the thickness of the glass. See p 8.

Plate 4: This illustrates the opposite effect to Plate 3; in prolonged low relative humidity, or when there is a daily cycle of low and high humidity, shrinkage of the emulsion can cause it to lift from a stable base such as glass (shown here) or polyester. See p 15.

RH should also be avoided. While suitable temperature and RH are both important, it is RH that is critical for the permanence of the silver image, while cycling of RH, even at low values, causes prints to curl.

Added protection can be given to prints of all kinds by storage at lower temperature. This is recommended for colour prints, so is described in Chapter 5; but for black-and-white prints it is unnecessary and has serious disadvantages of cost and inconvenience, especially if the prints need to be available for study; for the storage and study areas should, wherever possible, share the same environmental conditions (see below).

Enclosures and containers

Prints of aerial photographs will not normally be separately sleeved, but any that have labels stuck on them or annotations (especially with felt-tip pens, which may transfer marks when touching another print) should be interleaved with sheets of paper. Annotations in white or red labelling ink appear not to harm other prints but are not archivally permanent, so need to be systematically recorded by copying or transcription. The prints have normally been produced in standard sizes, so are readily stored in boxes of corresponding size. The boxes and the interleaved sheets of paper should be of conservation quality for use with photographs, ie, pH-neutral and non-buffered. The boxes should themselves be housed in drawers or cupboards capable of excluding dust, dirt and water.

If sleeves should be needed, the type recommended for negatives (p 16, above) is equally suitable for prints.

Prints of uncertain chemical stability (because processed in unknown conditions, or treated or marked with unidentified substances) should be stored separately, in their own housings.

Handling and studying archival prints

Archival prints should be handled with great care and protected from damage by creasing, scratching and abrasion. They should be handled by their edges, with clean hands, preferably using clean, thin, lint-free, cotton gloves. If a large or fragile photograph is to be picked up, it should be supported on a piece of clean stiff card.

Prints should not be marked in any way, even with wax pencils. If details need to be traced off, this should be done through clear plastic sheet (eg, cellulose triacetate) stiff enough not to transmit the pressure of pen or pencil directly to the print so as to cause any indentation.

On no account should food or drink be brought anywhere near the photographs, nor any other fluid (eg, nail varnish, correcting fluid, eau de cologne, etc).

To avoid fluctuation in environmental conditions between the store and the study area, the study area should, if possible, be actually inside the store. (This will clearly be impossible if the store is kept at a temperature of 2°C/36°F.) The lighting provided for the examination of prints should be no greater than necessary, ideally not above 80 lux , which is roughly the output of a 60 watt bulb in a reflector at a distance of one metre. For detailed study it may be required to raise this to 100 lux, but the exposure of individual prints to this light level should be kept to a minimum. Incandescent lamps or UV-filtered colour-corrected fluorescent tubes should be used; the UV component of the light should be less than 75 microwatts per lumen.

Inspecting stored prints

A number of different representative samples of prints should be inspected every two years. The sampling programme should be prepared in advance and a different lot should be examined on each occasion. If it is known that the recommendations for temperature and relative humidity have not actually been observed, inspections should take place more frequently.

The purpose of inspection is to detect any physical changes in the prints (curling, distortion, brittleness, cracking, flaking or peeling of the emulsion), any visual changes (fading, spotting or discolouration) and any changes in the material of enclosures (brittleness, discolouration).

If prints have been kept in cool or cold storage, they should be allowed to warm up gradually to the temperature of the room in which the inspection is to take place, before their enclosures are opened. This could take several hours, depending on the size of package and the temperature difference to be eliminated.

Once the nature of any deterioration has been determined and its cause identified, action should be taken, where possible, to halt it or put it right. Both the fault and the remedy should be recorded for future reference.

Cleaning and uncurling prints

It is possible to remove surface dirt, grease and mould from the emulsion of a print using the same materials and the same methods as described above for negatives (p.18).

Prints that have been kept in unsuitable enclosures, or none, and in poor environmental conditions will often have suffered curling, and this makes them difficult to use, or to store in a standardised system.

If they are only mildly curled, it should be possible to open them out without cracking or breaking the emulsion. The print can then be placed face down on a clean sheet of white blotting paper and held in position with padded weights. By lifting and replacing the weights one at a time, a second sheet of blotting paper can be laid over the print, and a sheet of glass over that. The sandwich is then left for several days in the hope of improvement. Relaxation of the curled print can be encouraged by a slow increase in relative humidity, being careful not to exceed 60 per cent. A variation on this technique is to lay the print face-down on a sheet of silicone or wax release paper and to lightly spray the back with distilled water. Change the paper and repeat as necessary adding a pressing paper on the back of the print to help relaxation. The uncurled print should eventually be stored in such a way that it continues to be held flat.

When prints have been deliberately rolled up for storage and have spent a long time in this condition, it may be impossible to unroll them fully without damage to the emulsion. It should nevertheless be possible to re-roll them around a cardboard tube, wrapped in conservation-quality tissue, that has a slightly larger diameter than the rolled-up prints. Further tissue should be added as an interleaving layer between overlapping portions of each print and to wrap the whole package, which should be lightly but firmly tied with unbleached cotton tape, to which an identification label can then be attached. The prints are stored rolled, but re-rolling round ever-larger tubes at well spaced intervals may eventually bring them back into practical use.

Mounting and displaying prints

Archival prints should not be mounted or put on display. If an archival print is essential to some exhibition, it should be copied and the copy should be exhibited.Individual photographic collections may nevertheless contain prints that have already been mounted. The board used for the mount is unlikely to be of conservation quality and is often of quite poor materials. Besides being acidic, it may well have grown brittle with age, so it is essential to support all mounted prints when handling them, for fear that the mount itself cracks or breaks, thus damaging the print. Contrary to expectations, a mounted print is more fragile than an unmounted one; it should certainly not be picked up by one corner, for example. If the board is bowed, special storage arrangements will need to be devised to exclude all possibility of pressure being applied to it causing it to crack. It may be best, if practicable, to remove certain prints from their mounts; this may depend on the type of adhesive used. In any case advice and assistance should always be sought from an experienced photographic conservator. Remember that the mount may carry information relating to the photograph.

Collections of aerial photographs are quite liable to include mosaics composed of overlapping prints stuck down on a backing to form a photomap. This presents a range of problems in care and storage. If the mosaic is of any size the backing is likely to be made of canvas, plywood or blockboard (both unsuitable materials giving off peroxides), though sheet aluminium is also used. Prints are not only stuck to the backing, but to each other. The most popular adhesives have been gum arabic and flour paste, but rubber cement is also not uncommon, despite being inconvenient to use for this purpose. The utility of the mosaic would be lost if it were taken apart, so an acceptable way needs to be found of storing it. If the backing and adhesive are not chemically inert, the mosaic should be stored in a different place from the remainder of the collection. In anticipation of its own eventual deterioration a copy photograph should be taken of the whole mosaic. (To achieve satisfactory results, this may require the use of a special camera or the assistance of a specialist professional studio.) If the individual prints of which the mosaic is composed are lifting at the edges, it is time to call in a professional conservator.

Copying prints

Processing of copies should obviously be of a kind to promote archival permanence (Appendix A).

When financial considerations allow, copying is one of the most effective ways to preserve the image on archival prints of aerial photographs. Use of a copy for study or for display preserves the original from accidental damage and from exposure to unfavourable environments. Storage of originals and copies in different locations is an effective insurance against loss through theft, fire, flood and building subsidence.

5   Storing processed colour film and prints

Why colour photographs demand special treatment

In colour photographs the image is rendered by means of colour dyes in the emulsion. There have been a number of different methods developed of achieving this, but they all suffer from the same limitation: the dyes themselves are archivally unstable. In other words, unless the greatest care is taken to protect the images from the effects of excessive temperature, humidity and light, their colours will fade. All colours are affected but some more than others, so that the balance of colours is altered as well as their strength.

Not all colour materials behave identically (those most recently introduced tend to be more stable than those current previously), but none is unaffected, so all will need storage in special conditions. The general principles involved are the same as for black-and-white (Chapters 3-4, above), but the conditions are more stringent.

Colour slides, being essentially intended for projection onto a screen, introduce a number of particular considerations which are discussed separately below, in Chapter 6.

Processing colour materials for maximum stability

There are no special 'archival processing' techniques for colour like those described in Appendix A for black-and-white. This is because the procedures involved in developing and printing colour are so technically complex that any deviation from the letter of the manufacturers' instructions is liable to produce an unsatisfactory result. The only pertinent advice, therefore, is to follow the instructions meticulously and always to maintain a professional standard of cleanliness.

Storing colour film and archival prints

Special attention has to be paid to temperature, humidity and light. In other respects the storage of colour film and prints is similar to that of black-and-white film and prints (see Chapters 3 and 4 above, respectively).

Temperature and relative humidity
Both temperature and relative humidity (RH) should be restricted to lower values than are permissible for black-and-white materials. For colour materials it is temperature that is the more critical factor. A distinction can nevertheless be made between 'medium-term' storage, appropriate to film and prints that are expected to receive occasional practical use, and 'archival' storage, where the film or prints are expected to remain undisturbed over long periods.

Medium-term storage is a compromise between conservation (storage in ideal conditions, not above 2°C/36°F) and practicality (the need to bring the film or print up to working temperature when it is to be put to use). Recommended maximum temperature is 10°C/50°F, while RH should be in the range 15-30 per cent for acetate films, 25-30 per cent for polyester films, and 30-45 per cent for prints.

For archival storage the temperature should be reduced to 2°C/36°F or less, while still keeping RH in the same range as before. There are two ways to do this: either you can store the photographs inside freezers, or you can chill the whole storage room to 2°C/36°F or less. In either case, if you should wish to inspect or study a particular film or print, it will be a major operation to recondition it so that it can be safely handled.

Cold storage involves placing the photographs in hermetically sealed containers which are then kept in a freezer. The photographs must first be conditioned to the recommended RH at room temperature. Roll film can be put into taped cans within heat-sealed bags, while sheet film and prints can be put in two such bags, one inside the other. It is important to leave as little air as possible in each bag before it is sealed.

The cans should be made of impermeable materials with a friction-type or threaded twist-on lid incorporating a seal (but not a rubber gasket). Other types of lid need to be sealed up with several wraps of pressure-sensitive adhesive tape of low gas permeability. This tape should be renewed at least every two years. A suitable type of bag is of aluminium foil coated with clear polyethylene on the inside and laminated to sheet paper on the outside. Care should be taken in handling the bags to avoid their being punctured. Double-bagging is a precaution against undetected pinholes, but while the use of such bags improves moisture protection, it does not guarantee it.

Preparation of photographs for this method of storage is expensive, time-consuming and labour-intensive. For most kinds of aerial film it would be quite impractical: conditioning cabinets are not designed for film 240mm wide and 76m long, and to condition such a film by simply keeping it for a time in the recommended atmosphere could hardly be achieved in less than a month. Deep-freeze units for storage would be relatively inexpensive to run, but would take up a great deal of space if the collection were of any size.

Cool storage involves keeping the whole storage room both at a maximum temperature of 2°C/36°F and at the recommended RH. While this is simpler in concept and eliminates the need for sealed containers, it will call for an expensive installation, seeing that it is not easy to maintain low RH at such a low temperature.

Light

All photographs are best stored in the dark and should be protected at all times from ultraviolet radiation (see Chapter 2). This is specially important for photographs in colour. Roll film should be stored in closed opaque containers with a light-tight lid. Sheet film and prints should be kept in opaque envelopes or folders or otherwise protected from needless exposure to light. If stored at normal room temperature, however, nearly all colour materials (with the exception of Ilford Ilfochrome, formerly Cibachrome) will still fade, even when they are kept in the dark. This explains the great emphasis placed on storage at low temperature by all authorities (for which see above). Prints should only be mounted or put on display if they are expendable copies.

Reproduction of original colour transparencies

It may be necessary to send original transparencies away for reproduction by a client. This is fraught with danger, even at the most reputable of clients and it is safer to make a duplicate and send that if time and cost permit. It is almost inevitable that the most attractive transparencies in a collection are the most wanted and if an original is sent out at all commonly, it will not be long before it is no longer in a state to be used again. Nevertheless, if an original does have to be sent, it should be protected by a transparent sleeve in some archivally sound material similar to the TEC® sleeves marketed by Secol and accompanied by documentation that clearly identifies it as an original demanding care in handling. Where appropriate, this documentation should be in the form of legally binding terms and conditions which place responsibility for safeguarding the original material and costs of repair or compensation in the hands of the recipient until return to the collection by any means affording proof of delivery and with the correct level of insurance cover for the loss value of the item in transit.

Copying colour photographs

When financial considerations allow, copying is one of the most effective ways to preserve the image on negatives, transparencies or archival prints of aerial photographs. Copying colour images onto black-and-white polyester film removes them from a high risk of fading. Use of a copy print for study or display preserves the original from accidental damage and from exposure to unfavourable environments. Storage of originals and copies in different locations is an effective insurance against loss through theft, fire, flood and building subsidence.

Various methods of copying are available and are suited to different purposes.

Colour separations are made through colour filters onto a set of three black-and-white master negatives. If these are made on polyester film in accordance with the procedures set out in Appendix A, they will have excellent archival permanence and can be used at any time subsequently to reconstitute the original colour image. This is the only way to achieve a permanent and full archival record by photographic means, but it is too complex to be adopted as routine.

A simple black-and-white copy may be sufficient to record all the information required for some purposes and may therefore have a certain value, despite losing the colour dimension. Nevertheless, a principal reason for using colour in aerial photography is that some details can be readily distinguished from each other in terms of colour when their tonal values on the grey scale are very similar; so for general purposes a monochrome copy is not fully satisfactory.

A colour copy will inevitably be susceptible to the same hazards as the original from which it is taken, but by its existence it will protect the original by substituting for it. In making a duplicate transparency, film with a low film-speed is thought to ensure a longer useful life. If the original has already faded, use of special film (Ektachrome Duplicating Film 6121) will automatically restore a plausible colour balance without the need to use elaborate filtration.

Copies made by non-photographic methods, such as hardcopy derived from an electronic scan or laser printing have now begun to achieve a quality that is comparable to the original photographic image. Their longevity in archival conditions has yet to be evaluated, however.

6   Storing colour slides

There are a number of reasons for dealing with colour slides in a chapter of their own.

The standard colour slide is a 35mm transparency held in a mount 50mm square. It is made directly from exposed film by reversal processing. In other words, it is an original, not a copy; yet its intended use involves exposure to a beam of light in the projector, which is the last thing (in general terms) you should think of doing to an original colour photograph. Advice is needed on how to minimize the effects of such abuse.

The mount itself is a source of concern from the archival point of view. It is important that it should not contribute to possible damage to, or future deterioration of, the transparency.

The use of colour slides is widespread. Appropriate films and processing are available to the mass market, and when the slides are received from the laboratory, they are ready for use in lectures and slide-shows without further ado. They are particularly attractive to the amateur aerial photographer, who can quickly build up a large collection. Storage systems need to be designed not only to accommodate large numbers of mounted slides but also to facilitate their speedy location and recovery when needed for a use.

Mounting slides

Slides are usually received from the laboratory in open (ie, unglazed) card or plastic mounts, though they may also be supplied in uncut strips of film which will then need to be mounted by the customer. Standard card mounts are unlikely to be of archival quality, and they are held together by adhesive that is liable to fail during long-term storage (say, after 20 years) or in the presence of moisture. The transparency then falls out of its mount. For mounting film that is supplied uncut and for replacing card mounts it is best to use plastic mounts, whose two halves simply snap together into place. Many brands of slide mounts are available, made of plastic or metal, which incorporate thin sheets of glass between which the transparency is sandwiched. The glass not only protects the transparency from some kinds of accidental damage; it also contributes to film flatness during projection, so avoiding the tiresome 'popping' of slides. For this reason the use of glazed mounts is popular, and the expression 'mounting slides' has commonly come to mean re-mounting them between glass. From the archival point of view, however, the use of glass is unacceptable, since it tends to trap moisture and there is always danger of the transparency buckling within the slide so as to come into contact with the glass and possibly sticking to it. Greasy deposits can also form on the inside of the glass derived from plasticisers or other substances in the film.

The use of glazed mounts would be appropriate for sets of slides to be loaned out for classwork or to be used by untrained projectionists, but they do not travel well through the post, being heavy and fragile and can cause serious injury if broken. If used for such purposes, the slides should be copies, not originals, in the first place.

Handling slides

When slides have open mounts, it is particularly important to handle them with due care and, if they are to be made available for lectures or for private study, to make sure that the lecturer and projectionist, or the student, is adequately instructed in how best to hold them. Colour slides are still such a familiar part of the domestic scene, despite the growing use of video, that it will not occur to many users to treat them with the degree of care that all irreplaceable documents deserve. In an archival collection the rule is everything is original and irreplaceable unless identified otherwise and should be handled accordingly.

Slides should be held only by the edges of the mounts. If a lot of slides are to be dealt with, it will be sensible to wear the same clean cotton gloves as have been recommended for handling other types of film and archival prints. When slides are placed on a viewing table or any other surface, this must be checked for dust, grit, spillage or anything that could scratch, pierce or stain the film.

Storing slides

One of the most convenient and inexpensive ways to store slides is to use hanging files made of clear plastic sheet, with rows of pockets into which individual slides are placed. Two dozen slides can then be viewed against a light source at one time without removing any of them from the file unless it is wanted. Care must, as usual, be taken to ensure that the plastic used is appropriate. It must not be PVC or any of the other prohibited materials listed on p 8; furthermore it should be semi-rigid rather than fully flexible, or else the material forming the pocket may sag against the surface of the film so as to cause ferrotyping or other problems.

Large collections of infrequently required material may call for more compact storage. A relatively simple system is to use storage boxes of card, each of which holds one column of slides stacked on end; a row of such boxes will fit into a larger box designed for the purpose, with a drop front for easy access. The card used must, of course, be of archival quality. Acetate sleeves would give the individual slides protection from finger prints and mechanical damage.

More elaborate boxes and cabinets with removable trays or drawers are available in great variety, but, being made for the mass market, are often of unsuitable materials, such as varnished wood (see Chapter 2). Preferable are units made of steel with a baked enamel finish or of chemically inert plastic with a high melting point.

Environmental conditions in the store-room should be as described above in Chapter 5 for colour films in general.

Projecting slides

Original transparencies warranting archival protection should never be projected in any circumstances. Colour slides fade perceptibly after 20 minutes' exposure to the light of a projector (12 minutes if the exposure is continuous). The longer the exposure at any one time, the more likely that some change will take place. Presentations should, as far as possible, leave individual slides on the screen for no more than 15-30 seconds.

It is important also to check that the projector is fully functional, ie, that the fan is working and that there is a heat-absorbing glass fitted between the lamp and the slide-holder. Whenever local conditions allow, ie, when the black-out is satisfactory, the low-intensity setting for the projection lamp should be selected.

Viewing slides on a light box also exposes them to harmful illumination, and they should not be left there for any longer than is actually needed.

Copying slides

The best way to preserve slides from the deleterious effects of projection is to use only copies for this purpose while keeping the originals in a controlled environment in the store. Fujichrome Duplicating Film is recommended, but if you are using Kodak films, Kodachrome slides are said to last longer in storage, while Ektachrome slides are less badly affected by projection; so, it will be sensible to use Kodachrome in the air, but to copy onto Ektachrome. The same manufacturer makes a special slide duplicating film (5071) designed to compensate for fading of originals that have been kept in unfavourable (warm and moist) conditions.

7   Restoration of photographic images

If, despite all precautions, disaster strikes and original material is lost, it is lost and nothing can be done. If, however, negatives, transparencies or prints are merely damaged, there are remedies. Until recently, a skilled technician would duplicate the damaged image, retouch it insofar as this was possible and create a new negative or transparency from the result. Enlarging the image before retouching facilitated the work, but the loss in quality in the end product was noticeable.

The advent of digital imaging has changed the methodology. A damaged transparency or print, whether monochrome or colour, is scanned at relatively high resolution and the repair is performed on screen by replacing pixels (the individual elements of which a digitized image is composed) in damaged areas with pixels of appropriate shape or colour from other areas of the image dropped in. Since it is possible on screen to enlarge damaged areas to a considerable size, each repair can be effected with meticulous precision and will remain invisible, even when the final image is viewed at a large scale. The loss in quality is minimal. The processed image is then stored digitally and can be used to produce any number of identical prints or transparencies of very high quality, so making new negatives unnecessary. Appropriate precautions must, of course, be taken to ensure the permanence of the digital data, by making back-up copies and by periodic checks on continuing quality.

This method is ideal for removing minor, but distracting, blemishes from the photographic image, whether caused by dust specks, scratches, foxing, creases, ink marks or the like. It can be used to bring up detail in areas of fading, to increase contrast and to improve edge-sharpness as an aid to interpretation. What it cannot do is actually replace significant detail that has been damaged or destroyed. This means that for many forms of aerial photography its use is fairly limited. In photographs whose main archival purpose is to record details of the landscape at a given time for future research even the cosmetic removal of blemishes might be thought to be potentially misleading. On the other hand, photographs chosen for reproduction because of their pictorial quality can benefit enormously from the judicious use of electronic enhancement.

8   Further Reading

The information and advice given in the preceding pages has been compiled from a number of sources, of which the most useful are listed below. The reader is referred to these for fuller treatment of any topic, where needed.

Allen, N. S., Edge, M, Jewitt, T. S., and Horie, C. V. (1990)
   Stabilization of cellulose triacetate base motion picture film. Journal of Photographic Science, 38(1), 26-9. *(Also applies to cellulose nitrate, and to still photography.)*
BS ISO 3897:1992
   Photography. Processed photographic plates . Storage practices. British Standards Institution.
BS 5699: 1979
   Processed photographic film for archival records.
   Part 1. Specifications for silver-gelatin type on cellulose ester base.
   Part 2. Specifications for silver-gelatin type on poly(ethylene terephthalate) base. British Standards Institution.
Collings, T. J. (1983)
   Archival care of still photographs. Society of Archivists, information leaflet No 2. *(Especially for care of glass negatives.)*
Eaton, G.T. (1985)
   Conservation of Photographs. Rochester, NY: Eastman Kodak Company. *(With special, though not exclusive, reference to Kodak products.)*
Edge, M. and Allen, N. S. (1992)
   Factors influencing longevity of aerial photographic products on archival storage. Photogrammetric Record, 14(80), 207-18. *(Concerns cellulose acetate negatives.)*
ISO 5466: 1986
   Photography - processed safety photographic film -Storage practices. 3rd ed. International Organization for Standardization.
Keefe, L. E. and Inch, D. (1990)
   The Life of a Photograph, 2nd ed, Focal Press.
Kempel, S. (1987)
   The Care of Photographs. New York: Nick Lyons Books. *(Available in UK from Conservation Resources (UK) Ltd, at the address given in Appendix B)*
Reilly, J. M. (1993)
   IPI Storage Guide for Acetate Film. Rochester, NY: Image Permanence Institute.
Tull, A. G. (Ed) (1974)
   The Conservation of Colour Photographic Records. The Royal Photographic Society of Great Britain, monograph No 1.
Wilhelm, H. (1993)
   The Permanence and Care of Colour Photographs. Grinnell, Iowa: Preservation Publishing Company. *(Available in UK from Conservation Resources (UK) Ltd, at the address given in Appendix B. For £70 you get 744 pages setting out the detailed results of 25 years of rigorous testing of named photographic products; associated comment is not limited to colour materials.)*

Appendix A: Processing photographs for an archive

NB: The recommended procedures are given here in outline only. More detailed instructions can be found in the following works, as listed in Chapter 8.

BS 5699: 1979 (Part 1, Annex A; Part 2, Annex A), Collings (1983) (Appendix C), Keefe and Inch (1990) (Chapters 1-2)

Black-and-white negatives
Conventional processing leaves slight, but nevertheless significant, traces of chemicals on the negative that will eventually contribute to its deterioration. It is possible to prevent the occurrence of such residues by extending the normal washing time and by rigorous quality control, using standard tests to confirm correct results. These tests are vital because the purity of the chemicals used is progressively contaminated by the very act of processing. Control test kits are available from manufacturers or can be made up to specifications given in the professional photographic literature.

In summary, the relevant procedures are as follows:
- develop in accordance with manufacturers' instructions
- use an acid stop bath (with control test of the solution)
- fix to completion and test silver content of the solution (not above 1.5 g/l)
- wash very thoroughly and test emulsion for residual hypo
- treat with a suitable diluted toner solution to protect the silver image against contaminants
- dry in a pollution-free stable environment, away from all chemicals.

Black-and-white prints
In essence, the problem and its solution are the same as for negatives. Paper differs from film, however, in that it absorbs chemical solutions much more readily, unless specially made to be water-resistant. This has prompted an alternative approach in which fixing of the image is carried out so rapidly (in 30 seconds instead of 6-10 minutes) that there is negligible penetration of the paper. It should, however, be noted that not all authorities are agreed that the fast-fix method is suitable for archival prints.

Summaries are given below, first for the established procedures using two- (or three-) bath fixing, and then for the new procedure with a fast fix. Neither of these procedures should be used with resin-coated paper, on which a further note is added.

Two-bath fixing.
In summary, proceed as follows:
- develop in accordance with manufacturers' instructions
- use an acid stop bath (with control test of the solution)
- fix to completion in sodium thiosulphate, using a succession of two (or even

three) fixing baths, and test silver content of the solutions
- wash, then treat with hypo-clearing solution (sodium sulphite) -but note that hypo-eliminators based on hydrogen peroxide are not recommended
- wash very thoroughly and test margins of print for residual hypo
- treat with a suitable diluted toner solution to protect the silver image against contaminants
- dry in a pollution-free stable environment, away from all chemicals.

Fast-fix. - Since the whole point is to leave the paper in the fixing bath as short a time as is feasible, timing is critical - just 30 seconds in ammonium thiosulphate. All other stages of processing are just as above.

Resin-coated paper. - Follow the manufacturers' instructions and resist all temptation to extend fixing or even washing times. The longer the paper remains immersed, the greater the chance that water and chemicals will seep under the plastic coating and become trapped there. Quite apart from the possibility of eventual chemical reactions, the trapped moisture will also cause the print to roll up tightly into a tube that is totally unusable. Since the water finds its way in from the edges, a further precaution against this effect is to use over-large sheets of paper and then to trim off a substantial margin.

Colour negatives, transparencies and prints

Any departure from the manufacturers' instructions is inadvisable with colour materials (see p 24, above).

Appendix B: Suppliers of conservation-quality enclosures and containers and of certain equipment

The principal general suppliers of conservation-quality paper, enclosures and containers are listed below. It is important to remember that these suppliers stock a wide range of products: they may be 'archival', but not all will be suitable specifically for photographs. If the catalogue is not clear about this, it is always safest to ask.

Atlantis European Ltd
146 Brick Lane
LONDON E1 6RU
Telephone: + 44 (0)171 377 8855
Fax: + 44 (0)171 377 8850

Conservation by Design Ltd
Timecare Works
60 Park Road West
BEDFORD MK41 7SL
Telephone: + 44 (0)1234 217258
Fax: + 44 (0)1234 328164

Conservation Resources (UK) Ltd
Unit 1, Pony Road
Horspath Industrial Estate
Cowley
OXFORD OX4 2RD
Telephone: + 44 (0)1865 747755
Fax: + 44 (0)1865 747035

Preservation Equipment Ltd
Church Road
Shelfanger
DISS
Norfolk IP22 2DG
Telephone: + 44 (0)1379 65127
Fax :+ 44 (0)1379 650582

Secol Ltd
15 Howletts Way
Fison Way Industrial Estate
THETFORD
Norfolk IP24 1HZ
Telephone: + 44 (0)1842 752341
Fax: + 44 (0)1842 762159

More detailed information about suppliers of specific types of product can be found in the Directory of Suppliers of Materials, Equipment and Services for Archive and Book Conservation, Storage and Display (3rd ed, 1994) published by the Society of Archivists. This not only lists a large number of suppliers; it also contains a comprehensive index of the products and services supplied. The headings of most interest to readers of this book are the following:

Air cleaning systems
Air conditioning systems
Air pollution detectors
Boxes
Cold storage
Disaster recovery service
Envelopes, paper
Environmental data loggers

Environmental monitoring
Gloves, cotton
Humidifiers/dehumidifiers
Humidity chambers
Lamps
Light boxes and tables
Lightmeters
Paper, Silversafe

Photographic storage materials
Polyester sleeves
Polypropylene sleeves
Shelving, mobile
Shelving, static steel

Tape, linen and cotton
Thermohygrographs
Thermohygrometers
UV meters
UV protection

The Directory is available (£15 post-free to non-members) from:

The Stockholder of Publications, Society of Archivists
c/o Gwynedd Archives and Museums Service
County Offices
Shirehall Street
CAERNARFON
Caernarfonshire and Merionethshire
LL55 1SH
Telephone: + 44 (0)1286 679088
Fax: + 44 (0)1286 679637

Appendix C: other useful addresses

British Association of Picture Libraries and Agencies (BAPLA)
18 Vine Hill
LONDON EC1R 5DX
Telephone: + 44 (0)171 713 1780
Fax: + 44 (0)171 713 1211
A trade association representing UK picture libraries and agencies holding stock photographs and illustrations: advice is available to members on commercial, legal and other aspects of managing photographic collections.

BSI Standards
Breckland
Linford Wood
MILTON KEYNES MK14 6LE
Telephone: + 44 (0)181 996 7000
Fax: + 44 (0)181 996 7001
The British Standards Institution is responsible for developing and publishing British Standards. It also supplies copies in English of International Standards. Both can be obtained from the above address on a payment with order basis for non-BSI members.

The Centre for Photographic Conservation
233 Stanstead Road
Forest Hill
LONDON SE23 1HU
Telephone: + 44 (0)181 690 3678
Fax: + 44 (0)181 314 1940
A partnership of two photographic conservators, restorers, consultants and researchers: services offered include training courses in photographic preservation and conservation, and a disaster recovery service for photographic materials damaged by fire and/or water. Also provide the contact point for the Editor of the *PhMCG Newsletter*.

The Fire Protection Association
Melrose Avenue
BOREHAMWOOD
Hertfordshire WD6 2BR
Telephone: + 44 (0)181 207 2345
Fax: + 44 (0)181 236 9701
E-mail: info@lpc.co.uk
The Fire Protection Association is the National Fire Safety Organisation of the United Kingdom, working within the framework of the Loss Prevention Council, a non-profit UK company limited by guarantee partly funded by the Association of

British Insurers . It publishes a wide range of technical publications, video and slide sets related to fire, including regularly updated handbooks on fire safety. It maintains an information service and provides courses in fire safety management as well as in technical aspects of fire prevention and control.

The Image Permanence Institute (IPI)
Rochester Institute of Technology
Frank E. Garrett Memorial Building
PO Box 9887
Rochester
NY 14623-0887
USA
Telephone: + 1 716 475 5199
Fax: + 1 716 475 7280
A university-based non-profit research laboratory founded in 1985 by Rochester Institute of Technology and the Society for Imaging Science and Technology: activities include research in the stability and preservation of imaging media; education and training of preservation specialists; development of national and international standards; contract testing of materials, and consultancy; provision of technical information to museums, archives and libraries.

NAPLIB
c/o RCHME
NMRC
Kemble Drive
SWINDON SN2 2GZ
Telephone: + 44 (0)1793 414600
Fax: + 44 (0)1793 414707
E-mail: info@rchme.gov.uk
Web site: http://www.rchme.gov.uk
See p 39, below

Photographic Materials Conservation Group
c/o Conservation Department
Public Record Office
Ruskin Avenue
Kew
RICHMOND
Surrey TW9 4DU
Telephone: + 44 (0)181 876 3444
Fax: + 44 (0)181 878 8905
E-mail:PRO.RSD.Kew@gtnet.gov.uk
PhMCG is a professional interest group open to individuals and institutions whose field of interest in preservation and conservation includes photographic materials, and to scientists and researchers who are interested in photographic preservation and conservation and sharing information on a regular basis.

Process Supplies (London) Ltd
13-25 Mount Pleasant
LONDON WC1X 0AA
Telephone: + 44 (0)171 837 2179
Fax: + 44 (0)171 837 8551
Supplier of photographic materials, including print cleaner.

The Society of Archivists
Information House
20-24 Old Street
LONDON EC1V 9AP
Telephone: + 44 (0)171 253 5087/4488 + 65
Fax: + 44 (0)171 253 3942
E-mail:aslib@aslib.co.uk
Web site: http://www.aslib.co.uk/
The professional body for archivists, archive conservators and record managers, and publisher of Collings (1983) (see Chapter 8) and of the Directory of Suppliers, 3rd ed 1994 (see Appendix B): one of several special interest groups is the Preservation and Conservation Group, which holds an Annual Instructional Meeting (ie, conservation conference).

An independent organisation
promoting the use and
preservation of aerial photographs

The discovery of the photographic process and the advent of balloon flight in the mid-nineteenth century heralded the development of aerial photography, the application and development of which was accelerated during World War 1. From that time, the use of the aerial image for military and civilian purposes has become commonplace.

Often originated for purposes unrelated to its subsequent historic and archival value, aerial photography provides a unique and vulnerable record of the natural and man-made landscape. The accumulation of comparative aerial photographs over the last eighty years or so has greatly enhanced the value of any component part of this record.

In response to the perceived need for a voluntary association of aerial photographic libraries to address the problems of conservation and preservation, an inaugural meeting of the National Association of Aerial Photographic Libraries (NAPLIB) was held on 1989 February 27.

Sponsored by the Photogrammetric Society and held at the Royal Institution of Chartered Surveyors, this meeting determined four levels of Membership and appointed an Executive Committee charged with the aim of ensuring:

> *'the preservation of the greatest number of aerial photographs of the United Kingdom'*

and to

> *'increase public awareness of the existece of these photographs and to facilitate access to them'*

and

> *'encourage the interchange of ideas and expertise and, in particular, the development of appropriate indexing and storage procedures'*

and

> *'liaise with other professional organisations active in the field'*

In pursuance of these aims and ideals, the Association, now known simply by the title: *NAPLIB: An independent organisation promoting the use and preservation of aerial photographs*, publishes a regular newsletter, the *NAPLIB Flyer*, and organises a series of Annual Conferences and field visits for its membership, which now numbers some 3 Sponsors, 24 Libraries, 17 Individual Members and 3 Affilliates, and has undertaken an ambitious programme of publication.

The first work to be published, the *NAPLIB Directory of Aerial Photographic Collections in the United Kingdom 1993* collated by David List, addressed a long-felt need for a directory of the major sources of aerial photography and the many collections in which this unique record may be found. Now out-of-print and outdated by recent changes in UK local government, the revised edition of the Directory is soon to be published and made available both in conventional printed format and electronically, on the Internet.

The Care and storage of photographs: Recommendations for good practice by David Wilson, the second NAPLIB volume to be published, addresses the long-felt need for sound, practical, advice relating to the problems of photographic conservation. Collated from a wide and varied range of learned sources, often not easily available to the managers of collections, the distilled wisdom from David Wilson's work will become a hand-book of reference to all involved in the conservation of our unique inheritance.

With the successful completion of these three major publishing projects, the Executive Committee of the Association is evaluating the problem of collections deemed to be 'at risk', and actively seeking to expand the Association's membership to include more of the commercial sector, in order to further increase its sphere of influence, and meet future demands on its expertise and resources.

Derek A. Edwards,
Honorary Secretary

Index

An independent organisation promoting the use and preservation of aerial photographs

Application for membership 1997

Yes, I/we want to support the aim of promoting the use and preservation of aerial photographs. Please enrol me/us for:

Sponsor Membership	(£100 per year)	❏
Library Membership	(£30 per year)	❏
Individual Membership	(£10 per year)	❏
Student, Unsalaried, Retired	(£5 per year)	❏

Mr/Mrs/Miss/other (initials). . . . . Surname . . . .

Organisation. . . . .

Address . . . .

. . . .

. . . .

Postcode. . . . . Tel. . . . .

I/We enclose a cheque made out to NAPLIB for £ . . . . to cover my/our subscription. Please return copy of form with cheque to:

Treasurer, NAPLIB
c/o RCHME: National Monuments Record Centre
Kemble Drive
SWINDON
SN2 2GZ